Helen Gathercole

Do You Suppose

Nightingale Books

A CIP catalogue record for this title is
available from the British Library.
ISBN 978-1-83875-883-7

Nightingale Books is an imprint of
Pegasus Elliot MacKenzie Publishers Ltd.
www.pegasuspublishers.com

First Published in 2023

Nightingale Books
Sheraton House Castle Park
Cambridge England

Printed & Bound in Great Britain

Dedication

Dedicated to Cliff

Not a cliff by the sea

But a Cliff who is home

For my family and me.

Do you suppose
That an elephant knows
How to trumpet a tune
Through his very long nose?

And I don't understand
Why a bear is called bear
When a bear is not bare
He has fur for his hair!

Sometimes I wonder
How butter can fly
When it lives in a dish
Not up in the sky!

I find it confusing
A bird called a kite
Is not up on a string
He has wings for his flight!

And while I am asking
Do all dragons fly?
How does daddy with long legs
End up in the sky?

Do kingfishers
Actually fish for a king?
And I thought it was birds
Not whales that sing!

Does a hummingbird hum?
Does a lark lark around?
Does a Queen bee
Sit on a throne with a crown?

A clown is a fish!
An umbrella a bird!
Ladybird is a bug
It is all quite absurd!

Can a skate really skate?
Do fish go to school?
Does a sandpiper
Pipe out a tune for us all?

I actually think
Crocodiles could play snap
But if a cheetah joined in
There'd be no fun in that!

Can a bat use a bat?
Can a cricket play cricket?
Would stick insects
Stand in a row as a wicket?

It is easy to see
There is so much to learn
I have asked lots of questions
And now it's your turn!

About the Author

Helen Gathercole is a new author

who enjoys telling stories.